baby einstein.

Rhymes

The WALT DISNEP Company

Hyperion Books for Children, New York
Copyright © 2004 by The Baby Einstein Company, LLC.
All Rights Reserved.
Baby Einstein and the Boy's Head Logo are trademarks of The Baby Einstein Company, LLC. All Rights Reserved.
EINSTEIN and ALBERT EINSTEIN are trademarks of The Hebrew University of Jerusalem. All Rights Reserved.
For information address Hyperion Books for Children, 114 Fifth Avenue, New York, New York 10011-5690.
Printed in China
Library of Congress Cataloging Card Number on file.
ISBN 0-7868-3799-3

Visit www.hyperionbooksforchildren.com and www.babyeinstein.com

baby
einstein®

Great Minds Start Little.™

Bard the dragon spends his time

Finding pairs of words that rhyme.

bear

chair

mouse

dollhouse

A green frog hops by on the ground.

Can Bard find a rhyme for "frog" around?

frog

sky

dragonfly

log

There's a froggy on a lily pad,
A turtle on a log,
A long-nosed alligator, green,
All floating in the bog.

I look around the quiet lake—
Who's paddling two by two?
A kitten and a puppy dog
Aboard a red canoe!

All these things are floating,

But basically, I think,

Shells and stones and rocks and sand

Don't float because they sink!

Bard spies a blue bug in the air.

He'd like a rhyme for bug—but where?

bug

jug

rocks

fox

Waterfalls with misty breath
Whisper as they flow . . .

Frozen water turns to ice,
And flakes form out of snow.

Bard's sleepy—now it's late at night.

Can you find more rhymes before he says good night?

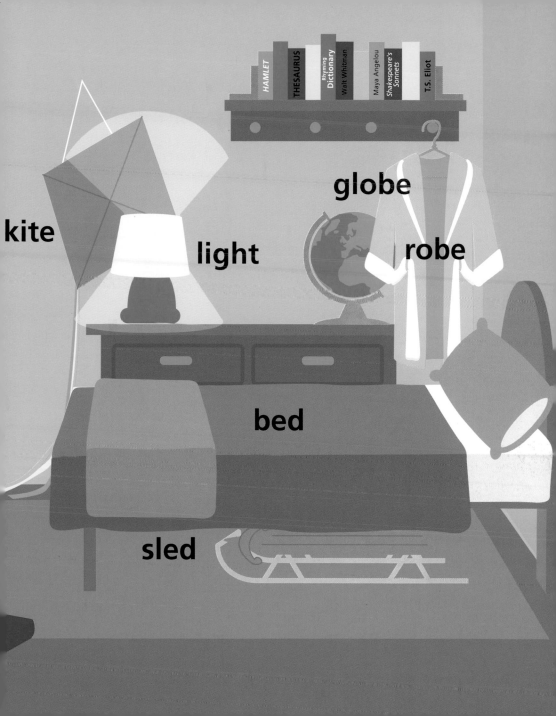

kite

light

globe

robe

bed

sled

HAMLET

THESAURUS

Rhyming Dictionary

Walt Whitman

Maya Angelou

Shakespeare's Sonnets

T.S. Eliot